The Best of
Music To Watch G

© 2007 by Faber Music Ltd
First published in 1999 by International Music Publications Ltd
International Music Publications Ltd is a Faber Music company
Bloomsbury House 74–77 Great Russell Street London WC1B 3DA
Cover artwork used by permission of Sony Music Entertainment (UK) Ltd
Printed in England by Caligraving Ltd
All rights reserved

ISBN10: 0-571-52968-2
EAN13: 978-0-571-52968-1

To buy Faber Music publications or to find out about the full range of titles available,
please contact your local music retailer or Faber Music sales enquiries:

Faber Music Ltd, Burnt Mill, Elizabeth Way, Harlow, CM20 2HX England
Tel: +44(0)1279 82 89 82   Fax: +44(0)1279 82 89 83
sales@fabermusic.com   fabermusicstore.com

Almost Like Being In Love

Words by Alan Jay Lerner
Music by Frederick Loewe

day this has been! What a rare mood I'm in! Why, its al-most like

be - ing in love!_____ There's a smile on my face for the

whole hu - man race. Why, it's al - most like be - ing in love!_____

___ All the mu - sic of life seems to be,_____ like a

Beyond The Sea (La Mer)

Original Words and Music by Charles Trenet and Albert Lasry
English Words by Jack Lawrence

Blue Moon

Words by Lorenz Hart
Music by Richard Rodgers

Blue Velvet

Words and Music by
Lee Morris and Bernie Wayne

Can't Take My Eyes Off You

Moderate tempo

Words and Music by
Bob Crewe and Bob Gaudio

lone - ly night, I love you, ba - by,— trust in me—when I— say:

Oh pret - ty ba - by,— don't bring me down, I pray,— oh pret - ty

ba - - by— now that I've found you, stay,— and let me love you,— ba -

D. S. al coda

-by, let me love you._____ You're just too

Coda

ba - by,— and if it's quite all right, I need you, ba - by,— to warm the lone-ly night, I love you,

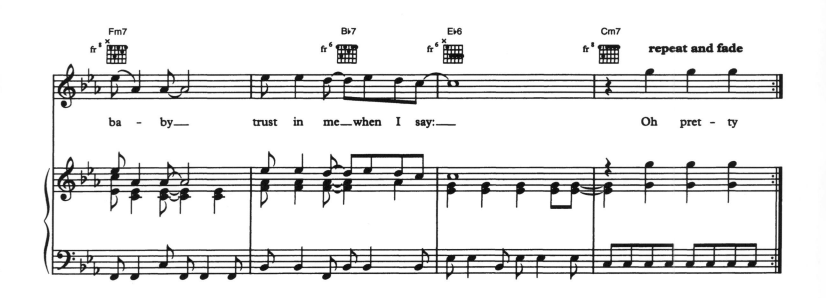

ba - by___ trust in me___when I say:___ Oh pret - ty

Fly Me To The Moon

Words and Music by
Bart Howard

A Certain Smile

Words by Paul Francis Webster
Music by Sammy Fain

hush of night ex-act-ly like a bit-ter-sweet re-frain, comes that

cer-tain smile to haunt your heart a-gain._____ A cer-tain

gain._____

Do You Mind?

Words and Music by
Lionel Bart

The Good Life

Words and Music by
Sacha Distel and Jack Reardon

It Had To Be You

Words by Gus Kahn
Music by Isham Jones

The Lady Is A Tramp

Words by Lorenz Hart
Music by Richard Rodgers

41

Moon River

Words and Music by
Henry Mancini and Johnny Mercer

Let There Be Love

Words by Ian Murray Seafield Grant
Music by Lionel Rand

Let there be you, let there be me,

49

Let there__ be

Love Letters In The Sand

Words by Nick Kenny and Charles Kenny
Music by J Fred Coots

Music To Watch Girls By

Words by Tony Velona
Music by Sid Ramin

Watch that sound each time you hear a loud col-lec-tive sigh

they're mak-ing mus-ic to watch girls by.

No One But You

Words by Jack Lawrence
Music by Nikolaus Brodszky

On The Street Where You Live

Words by Alan Jay Lerner
Music by Frederick Loewe

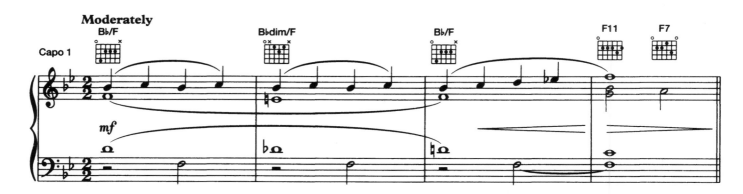

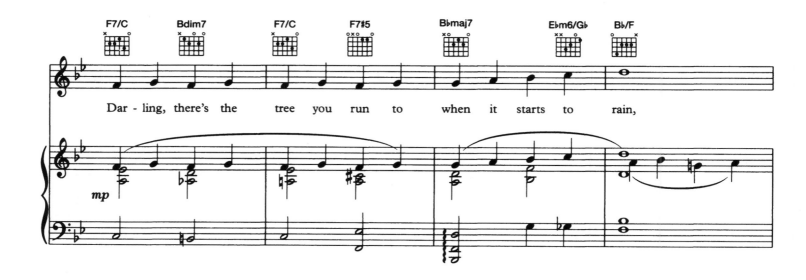

Dar - ling, there's the tree you run to when it starts to rain,

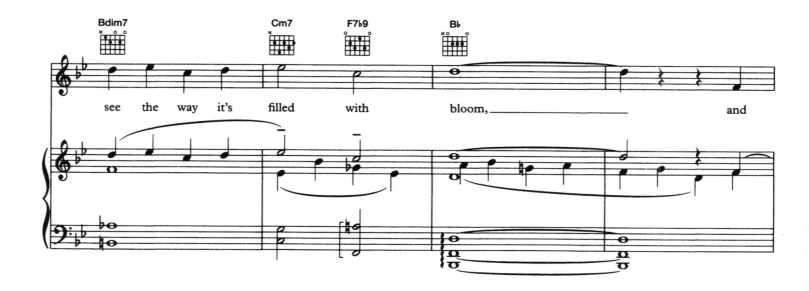

see the way it's filled with bloom,_____ and

She

Words and Music by
Charles Aznavour and Herbert Kretzmer

Spanish Eyes

Words and Music by
Bert Kaempfert, Charles Singleton
and Eddie Snyder

Theme From 'A Summer Place'

By Max Steiner

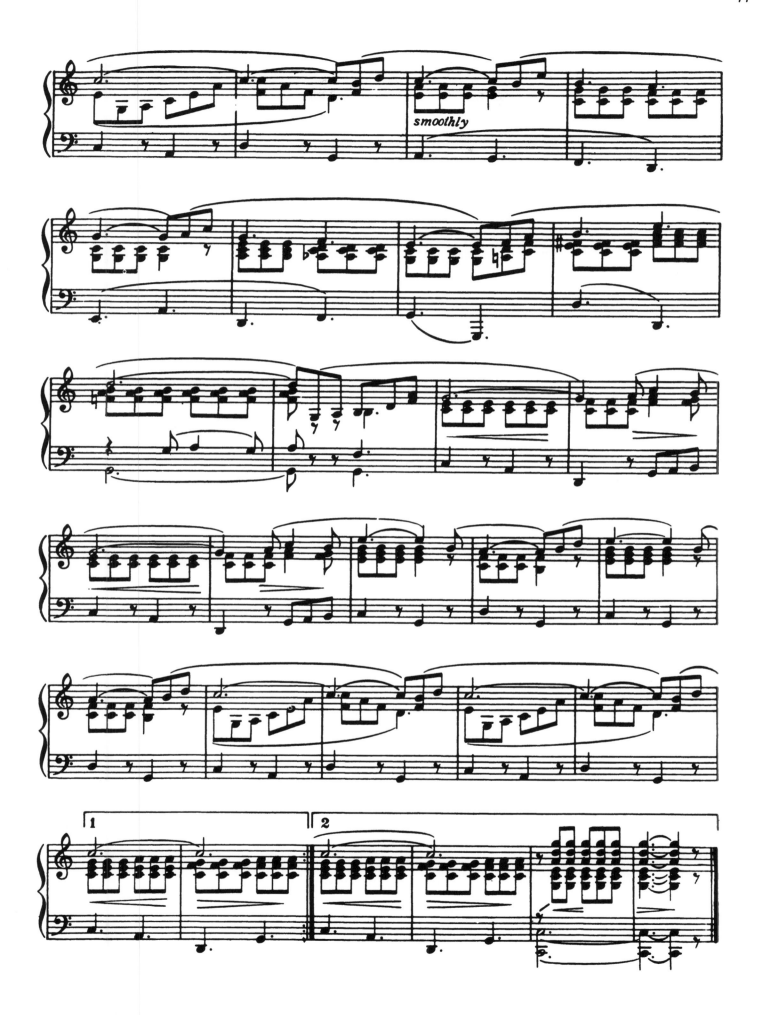

Up, Up And Away

Words and Music by
Jim Webb

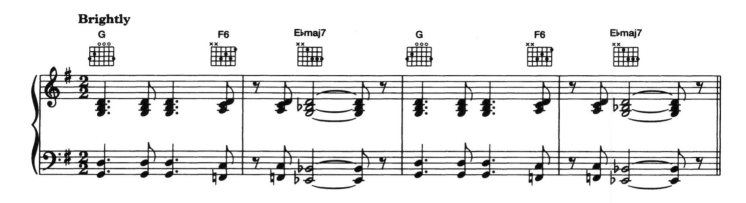

Would you like___ to ride___ in my___ beau - ti - ful___ bal - loon?
world's a ni - cer place___ in my___ beau - ti - ful___ bal - loon,
Love is wait - ing there___ in my___ beau - ti - ful___ bal - loon,

___ Would you like___ to glide___ in my___ beau - ti - ful___ bal - loon?
___ it wears a ni - cer face___ in my___ beau - ti - ful___ bal - loon.
___ way up in the air___ in my___ beau - ti - ful___ bal - loon.

Wishin' & Hopin'

Words by Hal David
Music by Burt Bacharach

Valley Of The Dolls

Words and Music by
Andre Previn and Dory Previn

Got-ta get off, gon-na get, have to get off from this ride;___
Got-ta get off, gon-na get, out of this mer-ry-go-round;___

Got-ta get hold, gon-na get, need to get hold of my pride.___
Got-ta get on, gon-na get, need to get on where I'm bound.___